Mental Arithmetic 1

CONTENTS

The following is a short synopsis of the contents of the tests indicating the order in whic̶ ̶ ̶ ̶ ̶ ̶ ̶ ̶ and their coverage.

A
Answer

1 Count the sticks. How many?

2 3 + 6

3 7 − 2

4 5p + 2p + 1p   p

5 9p − 6p   p

6 8 = 5 + ▩

7 4 × 1

8 5 = 9 − ▩

9 2 + 2 + 2 + 2

10 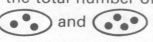 What is the time?   o'clock

B
Answer

1 Find the total number of dots.

2 Take 0 from 7.

3 Write the word for the missing number. 3, 5, ▩, 9 _____

4 Four more than five.

5 How many must be taken from 5 to leave 3?

6 To eight add nought.

7 What number equals double 2?

8 From 6 subtract 3.

9 Find the difference between 3 and 8.

10 Which of these numbers is an odd number? 2, 4, 5, 6, 8

C
Answer

1 Write the word for the number which comes between 6 and 8.
_____

2 Jane has 7p and she spends 4p. How much has she left?   p

3 Which is the shortest line, A, B or C?

A _____
B _____
C _____

4 Alan is 9 years old and Jill is 3 years younger. How old is Jill?

5 By how much is 7p more than 3p?   p

6 Tim has a FIVE and a TWO. How many pennies are these coins worth?   p

7 A line is 6 cm long. By how many cm is it shorter than another line 8 cm long?   cm

8 Mary has 2 TWOS and 4 pennies. How much money has she altogether?   p

9 Which is the third letter in the row?
A, B, C, D, E, F, G

10 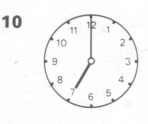 Peter gets to school 2 hours later than the time on this clock. At what time does he arrive?   o'clock

A

Answer

1   How many beads? Write the number word.

 _____

2   $2 +$ ▦ $= 8$

3   $4p + 3p + 1p$ ☐ p

4   $9 - 5$

5   Which two numbers are missing?
   2, ▦, 4, 5, ▦, 7, 8   ☐ and ☐

6   ▦ $- 3 = 2$

7   What is the time?   ☐ o'clock

8   $7 + 2 = 2 +$ ▦

9   $5 - 5$

10   $7p = 5p +$ ▦ p ☐ p

B

Answer

1   Write the missing even number.
   2, 4, ▦, 8

2   Seven minus four.

3   Find the total of 3, 0 and 5.

4   Take 8 from 8.

5   How many days in 1 week?

6   Find the total value of these coins.
   ☐ p

7   Write the number word which equals six plus three. _____

8   Add 4p and 5p.   ☐ p

9   From 9 take 7.

10   Subtract 0 from 6.

C

Answer

1   Which is the longest line, A, B or C?

   ☐

2   Jack spent 3p.
He had a FIVE left.
How much had he at first?   ☐ p

3   How many days in a school week starting Monday and finishing Friday?   ☐

4   On a string there are 9 beads.
3 are red, 3 are blue and the rest are white.
How many white beads are there?   ☐

5   Jane has these coins in her purse. She spends 4p.
   ⬭5⬭ ⬭2⬭ ⬭1⬭1⬭   How much has she left?   ☐ p

6   Tim is 4 years older than Ann who is 4. How old is Tim?   ☐

7   This clock is 1 hour slow.
What is the correct time?
   ☐ o'clock

8   The length of a line is 8 cm. Find the length of a line which is 3 cm shorter.   ☐ cm

9   Joan has 2p and Mary has twice as much.
How much have they altogether?   ☐ p

10   George has a FIVE and 2 pennies.
How much more does he need to make 9p?   ☐ p

A

Answer

1   $2 + 5 + 2$

2   $8 - 0$

3   $6 + \blacksquare = 10$

4   $3 = 10 - \blacksquare$

5   $10 + 7$

6   $14 - 10$

7   $5p + 2p + 1p + 2p$ p

8   $10p - 8p$ p

9   $12 - \blacksquare = 2$

10 $10 + \blacksquare = 15$

B

Answer

1   Write the number word for 14.

2   What is the missing number?
    18, 17, 16, $\blacksquare$, 14, 13

3   Double 5.

4   Find the total of these coins.
   p

5   Subtract 6 from 10.

6   What number is added to 9 to make 19?

7   Find the change from a TEN after spending 4p.   p

8   Which is the even number?
    9, 11, 13, 15, 16, 17.

9   Increase 1 by 10. Write the number word.

10   What is the time after 3 hours?   o'clock

C

Answer

1   Write the word for the number shown on the abacus picture.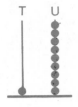

2   Joan spends 3p and 5p. How much change from a TEN?   p

3   In a bag there were 17 sweets. 10 are eaten. How many are left?

4   Sue is 11 years old. How old will she be in 6 years time?

5   What number is taken from 19 to leave 12?

6 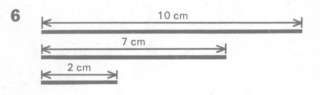

Find the total length of the three lines.   cm

7   What is the difference in cm between the longest and shortest lines?   cm

8   If Monday is the first day of the week, name the fourth day.

9   How many TWOS have the same value as a 10p coin?

10 Peter has two coins in his pocket the total value of which is 12p.
Name both coins.   p   p

A

Answer

1 0 + 7 + 0

2 9 + 3 − 5

3 10 + ▓ = 13

4 2 + 8

5 6 + ▓ = 10

6 ▓ − 5 = 10

7 1 TEN = 1 FIVE + ▓ p   p

8 1 TWENTY = 1 TEN + ▓ p   p

9 0 + ▓ = 10

10 10 cm + 6 cm   cm

B

Answer

1 How many more dots to make eighteen?

● ● ● ● ● ● ● ● ● ●

2 1 TWENTY = 1 TEN + ▓ FIVES   FIVES

3 Write the correct sign, + or −
in place of ●.
13 ● 4 = 17

4 What number is added to 4 to make 16?

5 Decrease 20 by 5.

6 Which is the eighth letter in the row?
A, C, E, G, H, J, M, O, P, W

7 Find the change from 1 TEN after spending 7p.   p

8 Find the sum of 3, 4, 0 and 10.

9 Ten plus eight minus seven.

10 Which is the odd number?
4, 6, 12, 15, 18, 20

C

Answer

1 Find the total value of the coins in the box.

p

2 If the date is 4th May, what is the date 10 days later?_____

3 The length of a piece of wood is 17 cm.
How many cm are sawn off to leave 10 cm?   cm

4 Tim has a FIVE. Pat has twice as much.
Find the total of their money.   p

5 What is the missing number?
4 + 10 + ▓ = 19

6 I spent 12p, 3p and 4p.
How much change did I receive from 1 TWENTY?   p

7 Jack is 18 years old. How old was he 7 years ago?

8 16 people were on a bus.
7 got off and 3 got on.
How many people were then on the bus?

9 Which of these shapes is
(a) a square (b) a circle?

(a) (b)

10 On checking his answers to part C of this test, James had 3 wrong.
How many had he correct?

A

Answer

1. $13 + \blacksquare = 18$

2. $14 - \blacksquare = 4$

3. $18 = 1 \text{ ten} + \blacksquare \text{ units}$

4. $3 + 8$

5. $9p + 4p$ p

6. $5 \text{ cm} + 7 \text{ cm}$ cm

7. $12 - 9$

8. $15p - 8p$ p

9. $11 \text{ cm} - 8 \text{ cm}$ cm

10. $5 + \blacksquare = 13$

B

Answer

1. What number when added to 10 makes 19?

2. Take 7 from 18.

3. Increase 6 by 5.

4. Write the part of the square which is shaded
   (a) as a word (a)
   (b) in figures. (b)

5. From 13p take 7p.   p

6. Find the sum of 6 and 9.

7. 17 minus 8

8. 6 plus 7

9. What is the difference between 3p and 11p?   p

10. Find the total of 7 and the next odd number greater than 7.

C

Answer

1. What is the value of the missing coin?
   $\left(5\right) + \left(10\right) + \left(\quad\right) = 17p$ p

2. By how many is $8 + 8$ more than 9?

3. The date is the 8th June. What is the date one week later? _____

4. Tim has 4p less than Joan who has 13p. How much has Tim?   p

5. A cake is cut into 4 equal parts. Write the name of each part
   (a) as a word (a)
   (b) in figures. (b)

6. What is the next even number which is greater than 10?

7. A line is 12 cm long. At what measurement is its middle point?   cm

8. Ann has twice as much money as Jill who has 4p. How many pennies have they altogether?   p

9. Write in words the time shown on the clock. _____

10. Alan has 18p. He spends 7p and 4p. How much has he left?   p

A

Answer

1   2 tens + ▦ units = 20

2   ▦ − 10 = 2

3   7 + 7

4   3p + 9p   [p]

5   ▦ + 4 = 19

6   8 cm + 6 cm   [cm]

7   13 − 5

8   15p − 6p   [p]

9   11 cm − 4 cm   [cm]

10 16 − ▦ = 7

B

Answer

1   How many TWOS are worth 2 FIVES?

2   By how many is 6 less than 14?

3   What number when added to 8 makes 13?

4   Subtract 9p from 18p.   [p]

5   Decrease 12 by 4.

6   Add the first three even numbers.

7   Find the difference between the biggest and smallest of these amounts of money.
9p, 3p, 11p, 7p, 18p   [p]

8   8 plus 3 minus 5.

9   6 + 7 = 10 + ▦

10  Write the part of the circle which is shaded
(a) as a word
_____ (a)
(b) in figures.   [(b)]

C

Answer

1   John is 8 years old. How old will he be in 4 years time?

2   Take nought from thirteen.

3   Sue gave 2 FIVES, 2 TWOS and 3 pennies to pay for a notebook.
How much did the notebook cost?   [p]

4   How many half oranges can be cut from three whole oranges?

5   What is the time half an hour after midday? Write the answer in figures, and use a.m. or p.m.

6   How many 2p coins have the same value as 1 FIVE and 7 pennies?

7   There are 5 men, 6 women and 8 children in a bus. How many people are there altogether in the bus?

8   John has a half and Tony a quarter of a cake. What fraction of the cake is left?

9   How many days are there in a fortnight?

10 Write the letters of the shapes which are triangles.

A

Answer

1 $8 + \blacksquare = 19$

2 $\blacksquare - 7 = 10$

3 1 ten + $\blacksquare$ units = 14

4 8p + 7p   [ ] p

5 2 + 9

6 14 − 5

7 $3 + 6 = 9 + \blacksquare$

8 $10 - 5 = 12 - \blacksquare$

9 $\frac{1}{2} + \frac{1}{4}$

10 $6 + 7 = 7 + \blacksquare$

B

Answer

1 What number when added to 4 makes 13?

2 9 is $\blacksquare$ less than 16.

3 18 is $\blacksquare$ more than 9.

4 Write the missing word.
1 whole one = four $\blacksquare$ _____

5 From a dozen subtract 7.

6 How much change from a TEN after spending 2 TWOS?   [ ] p

7 There are 60 minutes (min) in 1 hour (h).
How many minutes in
(a) $\frac{1}{2}$ h (b) $\frac{1}{4}$ h?   (a) [ ] min (b) [ ] min

8 What odd number is bigger than 11 but less than 15?

9 8 plus 7 minus 10

10 Name the fourth month of the year.

C

Answer

1 Which of these lines is the shortest, A, B or C?

2 Alan is 11 years old. Joan is 3 years younger.
How old is Joan?

3 Jill has 9 pennies.
She changes them for three coins.
Write the value of each coin.   [ ] p [ ] p [ ] p

4 Sue has half a cake and shares the rest between two friends.
What fraction does each of the friends have?

5 The time on a clock is 6.45 but it is $\frac{1}{4}$ hour slow.
Write in figures the correct time.

6 Write the correct sign,
$<$, $>$ or $=$ in place of ●.
    $3 + 10$ ● $18 - 5$

7 Find the total of a TEN, 3 TWOS and 2 pennies.   [ ] p

8 Name the month which comes next after December. _____

9 What length is added to 8 cm and 6 cm to make 20 cm?   [ ] cm

10 Write the name of this shape.

10

A

Answer

1   ▦ + 4 = 17

2   13 − ▦ = 3

3   8 + 5 = ▦ + 8

4   17 = 1 ten + ▦ units

5   $\frac{1}{2} - \frac{1}{4}$

6   6 + 6

7   9p + 8p   [ ] p

8   16 cm − 9 cm   [ ] cm

9   7 + 5 + 5

10   18 − 7 − 6

B

Answer

1   Write the correct sign
   <, > or = in place of ●.
    4 + 0 ● 13 − 9

2   Name the eighth month of
   the year.   _____

3   Find the difference between
   3 cm + 7 cm and 19 cm.   [ ] cm

4   15p is ▦ p more than 8p.   [ ] p

5   Take three quarters from a
   whole one.

6   What number is 6 less than
   the sum of 10 and 4?

7   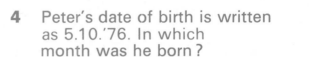 What is the time?
    Write the
    answer in
    figures.

8   Find the total of
   8p + 5p + 2p.   [ ] p

9   What number is added to
   13 to make 18?

10   Find the difference between
   17 and the next odd number
   bigger than 17.

C

Answer

1   Add together the even numbers
   which are less than 8.

2   A ball cost 13p. John gave
   two coins to pay for it.
   If the coins were of different
   values, what change did he
   receive?   [ ] p

3   A ————————————————— B

   Estimate (guess) the correct
   measurement of the line AB.
   Is it 10 cm, 4 cm or 8 cm?   [ ] cm

4   Peter's date of birth is written
   as 5.10.'76. In which
   month was he born?   _____

5   A boy saved 4p and 12p.
   How much more must he save
   to have a TWENTY?   [ ] p

6   Three girls each have a quarter
   of a cake.
   What fraction is left?

7   By how much are 3 FIVES
   greater than a TEN and 2
   TWOS?   [ ] p

8   David had 11 marbles.
   He lost 5 and then won 13.
   How many marbles had he then?

9   The time on a clock is 9.45 but
   it is half an hour fast.
   Write in words the correct time.

10   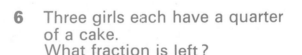 The three sides of
    triangle   a triangle together
    measure 17 cm.
    Two sides together
   measure 11 cm.
   Find the length of the third side.   [ ] cm

A
Answer

1   $8 - 0 + 7$

2   Write a word for the missing number.
    0, 10, 20, ▨, 40, 50 _____

3   $\frac{1}{4} + \frac{1}{2} + \frac{1}{4}$

4   50p = ▨ TENS

5   20p + 40p   p

6   $5\frac{1}{2} + \frac{1}{2}$

7   50 − 30

8   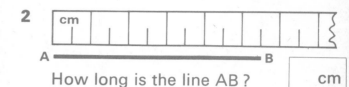 How much are these coins worth?   p

9   10 cm = $3\frac{1}{2}$ cm + ▨ cm   cm

10   2 + 2 + 2 + 2 + 2 + 2

B
Answer

1   Find the total of 7 TWOS and a FIVE.   p

2   Subtract twenty from fifty.

3   How many hours from 6.30 p.m. to 10.30 p.m.?   h

4   How much change from 2 TENS after spending 12p?   p

5   Add 10 cm to 40 cm.   cm

6   Eight groups each of 2. How many altogether?

7   How many FIVES for a TWENTY?

8   In which of these months are there 30 days? January, March, May, June _____

9   How many twos are there in 12?

10   Which three different coins together make 17p?   p   p   p

C
Answer

1   18 sweets are shared equally between Tim and Joan. How many each?

2
How long is the line AB?   cm

3   Twice seven minus nine.

4   Mother spends 11p. She gives one FIVE and the rest in TWOS. How many TWOS does she give?

5   9th September is on a Monday. On which day is 14th September? _____

6   John has 18p. He spends half of it and gives away 2p. How much has he left?   p

7   Write this time in the shortest way: a quarter to four in the afternoon.

8   An orange costs 8p. Find the cost of 2 oranges.   p

9   A box of sweets contains 2 layers each of 20 sweets. How many sweets are there in the box?

10   The lengths of two wooden rods are $7\frac{1}{2}$ cm and 10 cm. Find the difference in their lengths.   cm

A
Answer

1   $6 + 0 + 14$

2   Write a word for the missing number.
    100, 90, 80, ▨, 60 _____

3   $90 - 50$

4   $\frac{3}{4} + \frac{1}{2}$

5   $1\frac{1}{2}$ cm $= 10$ cm $-$ ▨ cm   cm

6   ▨ TWOS $=$ a TWENTY

7   $\frac{1}{2}$ cm $+ \frac{1}{2}$ cm $+ \frac{1}{2}$ cm $+ \frac{1}{2}$ cm   cm

8   $100 = 50 +$ ▨

9   $3p + 6p + 7p$ p

10 $4 + 4 + 4 + 4 + 4$

B
Answer

1   Find the total of 5p, 7p and 8p.   p

2   Take fifty from eighty. Write the word for the answer. _____

3   Multiply 4 by 6.

4   $\frac{1}{4}$ of 24

5   By how many pennies is 1 TWENTY less than 9 TENS?   p

6   In which of these months are there 31 days? April, June, August, November _____

7   How many quarters are there in $2\frac{1}{4}$?

8   Divide 36 by 4.

9   How many minutes are there from 7.45 a.m. to 8.15 a.m.?   min

10 How many times is 4 added together to make 28?

C
Answer

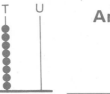

1   Write the word for the number shown on the abacus picture. _____

2   By how many cm is a line of $13\frac{1}{2}$ cm longer than a line of 8 cm?   cm

3   Share 1 TWENTY equally among 4 boys. How many pennies does each boy receive?   p

4   6th May is on a Tuesday. What is the date on Tuesday fortnight? _____

5   A balloon costs 6p. Find the cost of 4.   p

6   10 buttons are fixed on to a card. How many cards can be made using 100 buttons?

7   Find the total value of these coins.
    1 FIFTY, 2 TENS, 1 TWENTY   p

8   Mother spends 38p in a shop and gives a FIFTY in payment. She receives two coins as change. Which coins are they?   p   p

9   Find the sum of $\frac{1}{2}$, $\frac{3}{4}$ and 1.

10 What is the difference in minutes between the times on these clocks?

min

A

Answer

1 Write in words the missing number.
6, 16, 26, 36, ▨, 56 _____

2 Write these numbers in figures.
(a) 4 tens 7 units   (a)

(b) 6 tens 3 units   (b)

3 85 + 10

4 77 − 10

5 $1\frac{1}{2} - \frac{1}{4}$

6 0 × 4

7 8p + 10p + 20p   p

8 44p = ▨ TWENTIES ▨ p | TWENTIES | p

9 16 ÷ 4

10 40 = 4 × ▨

B

Answer

1 What number is thirteen more than eighty?

2 From 20p take 13p.   p

3 How many days in February this year?   (29 in a leap-year)

4 Find the total value of these coins.

p

5 Write the correct sign
+, −, × or ÷ in place of ●.
6 × 4 = 4 ● 6

6 How much change from 2 TWENTIES after spending 31p?   p

7 How many halves in six whole ones?

8 Decrease 70p by 8p.   p

9 What number is 3 times bigger than 4?

10 Find the remainder when 23 is divided by 4.

C

Answer

1

12 cm

9½ cm

Find the difference between the lengths of the rods.   cm

2 How many hours from 8.15 a.m. to 12.15 p.m.?   h

3 Write in figures the number which equals nine tens and seven units.

4 How many TWENTIES must be added to 40p to make £1·00?

5 The length of a line is 7 cm. What is its length if it is increased 5 times?   cm

6 Which of these numbers is nearest to 60?
58, 64, 56, 61, 63

7 Alison was born on 20th September 1976. Write her birthday using figures only.

8 One quarter of John's money is 8p.
How much has he altogether?   p

9 I gave 6 FIVES to pay for 7 sweets at 4p each.
How much change did I receive?   p

10 | ORANGES 3 for 20p | How many oranges can be bought for 60p?

A

Answer

1 Write in words the missing number.
82, 81, 80, ▨, 78 _____

2 Write these numbers in figures.
(a) 7 tens 2 units
(b) 5 tens 0 units

3 58 + 30

4 72 − 50

5 8 × 4 = 4 × ▨

6 2 − $\frac{3}{4}$

7 92p = ▨ TENS ▨ p

8 12 halves = ▨ whole ones

9 20 ÷ 4

10 Which number is missing from the series? 10, 15, 20, ▨, 30, 35, 40

B

Answer

1 Find the sum of 40, 30 and 20.

2 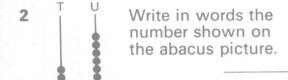 Write in words the number shown on the abacus picture.
_____

3 How many hours in a day? ☐ h

4 Share 32p equally among 4 children. How much each? ☐ p

5 Increase 50 by 27.

6 Take 32p from 2 TWENTIES. ☐ p

7 What number is 5 times greater than 8?

8 How many pennies are worth 9 FIVES? ☐ p

9 86 minus 40 plus 20.

10 $\frac{3}{4}$ of 12p. How many pennies? ☐ p

C

Answer

1 What number is seven less than eighty-three?

2 Which of these numbers is nearest to 80?
83, 75, 86, 78, 84

3 How many minutes from 3.00 p.m. to a quarter to four in the afternoon? ☐ min

4 How many FIVES are equal in value to the sum of 16p and 14p?

5 Find one quarter of the product of 8 and 3.

6 How much change from a FIFTY after spending 39p? ☐ p

7 Which sign +, −, × or ÷ is used in place of ●?
10 − 4 = 30 ● 5

8 One half of Peter's money is 26p. Find one quarter of his money. ☐ p

9 A bag contains 15p made up of an equal number of TWOS and pennies. How many of each coin are there?

10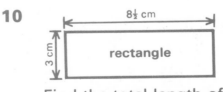

Find the total length of the four sides of the rectangle? ☐ cm

Next work Progress Test 1 on page 16. Enter the result and the date on the chart.

15

PROGRESS TEST 1

Write the numbers 1 to 20 down the side of a sheet of paper.
Write alongside these numbers the **answers only** to the following questions.
Work as quickly as you can.
Time allowed — **10 minutes.**

1 7 + 0 + 9

2 Find the difference between 8 and 15.

3 Nine times 4

4 Divide 45 by 5.

5 Eight tens and 4 units. Write the number in words.

6 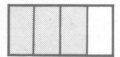 The shape stands for a whole one.
What fraction of it is shaded?

7 After spending 16p and 20p, what change is there out of a FIFTY?

8 76 − 40

9 60 + 33

10 What is the total value of the coins in the box?

11 4 toffees can be bought for 10p. How many toffees for 40p?

12  Write in the shortest way the time shown on
the clock.

13 ¼ of Tim's money is 15p. How much is ½ of his money?

14   The distance all round a square is 28 cm.
Find the length of each side.

15 There are 8 chairs in a row and 5 rows. How many chairs altogether?

16 How many days in August and September together?

17 Find the sum of ½ of 8p and ¼ of 16p.

18 In this series which number is incorrect?
0, 5, 10, 15, 20, 25, 30, 34, 40

19 Three lines measure 12½ cm, 3 cm and 7½ cm. By how many cm
is the shortest line less than the longest line?

20 If 25p is shared equally among 4 girls, how many pennies remain?

16

PROGRESS TEST 1 RESULTS CHART

You will work Progress Test 1 at **four** different times. When you first work the test
    (a) colour the first column to show the number of examples correct out of 20
    (b) enter the date.

Each time you work the test, enter the result and the date in the marked columns.

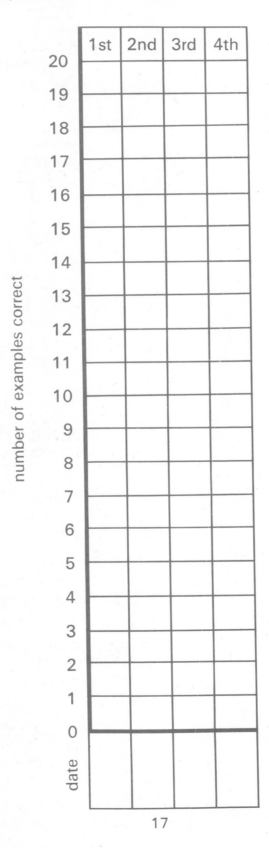

17

A

Answer

1   0 × 10

2   15 ÷ 5

3   18 + 8

4   23 − 7

5   A TWENTY, a TEN and 4 TWOS   p

6   7p + 5p + 8p   p

7   20p − 7p   p

8   $\frac{1}{2} + \frac{1}{2} + \frac{3}{4} + \frac{1}{4}$

9   35 = ▨ × 5

10   (9 × 4) + 3

B

Answer

1   What number is 8 less than 100 ?

2   Find the total of 27p, 12p and 10p.   p

3   How many tens in 90 ?

4   Write this time in figures. twenty minutes to seven

5   How many $\frac{1}{2}$ cm in 15 cm ?

6   Find the difference between 9 and 27.

7   Add the even numbers. 13, 21, 8, 19, 16

8   (3 × 10) + ▨ = 36

9   What number is 7 more than 45 ?

10   Write the two missing numbers in this series. 0, 3, 6, 9, ▨, 15, ▨

C

Answer

1   Find the total value of these coins.   p

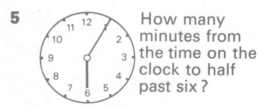

2   When 17 is taken from a number the answer is 13. What is the number ?

3   One quarter of the length of a piece of wood measures $8\frac{1}{2}$ cm. Find the length of the piece.   cm

4   In a class of 32 children 19 were boys. How many were girls ?

5   How many minutes from the time on the clock to half past six ?   min

6   5 boys win 2 TWENTIES which they share equally. How much do they each receive ?   p

7   How many TENS and TWOS are there in 76p ?

TENS	TWOS

8 | 34 | 32 | 42 | 37 | 45 |

Which of these numbers is nearest to 40 ?

9   Which is the cheaper **A** or **B** and by how much ?

   A biscuits 28p   **B** toffees 19p   p

10   3 + 3 + 3 + 3 + 3 + 3 = ☐ × 3

                                 =

A

		Answer
1	9p + 4p + 7p	p
2	4 × 3	
3	30 − 12	
4	$2\frac{1}{4}$ = ▦ quarters	
5	3)15	
6	How many days in March?	
7	1 TWENTY − 14p	p
8	5 FIVES + 3 TWOS	p
9	17 − 4 = 6 + ▦	
10	(0 × 3) + 7	

B

1 Write the two missing numbers in this series.
30, 27, ▦, ▦, 18, 15

2 Increase 23p by 8p   p

3 How many minutes from 7.10 p.m. to 7.45 p.m.?   min

4 7 times 3

5 How much change from a FIFTY after spending 32p?   p

6 How many threes in 27?

7 Add the odd numbers.
19, 12, 20, 5, 8

8 By how many is 24 greater than 17?

9 (8 × 3) minus 10

10 How many quarters in $1\frac{1}{2}$?

C

		Answer
1	What is the cost of 9 pencils at 5p each?	p

2 Write the missing number.
6 × 4 = ▦ × 3

3 Which 3 coins together make a total of 62p?   p   p   p

4 Add $\frac{1}{2}$ of 10 to $\frac{3}{4}$ of 8.

5 The heights of two girls are $89\frac{1}{2}$ cm and 94 cm. By how many cm is one taller than the other?   cm

6 Name the month which comes next
(a) before August   _____
(b) after March.   _____

7 Jane spends 7p which is one quarter of her money. How much had she at first?   p

8 Divide 30 by 3 and then add 9.

9 Tom gave 6 sweets to each of 5 friends. He had 4 left. How many had he at first?

10

kilogram	centimetre
litre gram	metre

Choose the metric measure to complete each of the following.
(a) The length of Tom's classroom is 10_____.
(b) John's weight is 35_____.
(c) A jug holds 1_____ of water.

A

Answer

1 $100 - 30$

2 $21 \div 3$

3 $5 + 5 + 5 + 5 =$ [ ] $\times\ 5$ = [ ]

4 9 TWOS + 2 FIVES [ ] p

5 $\frac{1}{4}$ of 32

6 $10\overline{)80p}$ [ ] p

7 $23 + 8$

8 $(7 \times 4) + 3$

9 $\frac{3}{4} + 1\frac{1}{2}$

10 $6 = 30 \div$ ▨

B

Answer

1 How many fours in 36?

2 Multiply 10 by 5 and add 6.

3 1 metre (m) = 100 centimetres (cm).

Q How many cm in $\frac{1}{2}$ m? [ ] cm

4 Share 24p equally among 3 boys. How much each? [ ] p

5 [strip diagram]

What fraction of the strip is not shaded?

6 By how much is 19p less than 3 TENS? [ ] p

7 $34 = (4 \times 10) -$ ▨

8 How many minutes from 6.05 to a quarter to seven? [ ] min

9 How much change from 35p after spending 24p and 7p? [ ] p

10 Write the two missing numbers in this series.
0, 6, 12, ▨, 24, ▨, 36 [ ] [ ]

C

Answer

1 By how many cm is 70 cm shorter than 1 m? [ ] cm

2 A number multiplied by itself makes 16. What is the number? [ ]

3 Divide the total of 4, 6 and 8 by 3. [ ]

4 A bag of potatoes weighs 25 kg. How many kg have been sold when the bag weighs 17 kg? [ ] kg

5 How many tenths are there in

(a) 2 whole ones [ ]

(b) $\frac{1}{2}$ whole one? [ ]

6 School begins at 8.55 a.m., but Tom is a quarter of an hour late. At what time did Tom arrive at school? [ ] a.m.

7 There are 50 litres of oil in a barrel. 32 litres are drawn off. How many litres are left in the barrel? [ ] ℓ

8 By how much is packet **A** more expensive than packet **B**?

| A soap powder 84p | B soap powder 77p |

[ ] p

9 What is a quarter of the difference between 36 and 24? [ ]

10 $6 + 6 + 6 + 6 + 6 + 6 =$ [ ] $\times\ 6$ = [ ]

A

Answer

1   14 pennies are worth TWOS.   [TWOS]

2   5 × 6   [ ]

3   26 + 9   [ ]

4   3 TENS = ▦ TWOS   [ ]

5   1 − $\frac{3}{10}$ [ ]

6   6)$\overline{42}$ [ ]

7   24 kg − 7 kg   [kg]

8   50p − 36p   [p]

9   1$\frac{1}{2}$ metres + 3 metres + $\frac{1}{2}$ metre   [m]

10   (3 × 6) + 5   [ ]

B

Answer

1   How many threes in 24 ?   [ ]

2   How many pennies are worth 2 FIFTIES ?   [p]

3   By how many cm is $\frac{1}{2}$ m longer than 33 cm ?   [cm]

4   What number is 9 less than 22 ?   [ ]

5   How many minutes in 1$\frac{1}{2}$ hours ?   [min]

6   The circle is a whole one. How many fifths in 3 whole ones ?   [ ]

7   (0 × 6) + 8   [ ]

8   How many days in December ?   [ ]

9   Find the total of 4 times 7p and 2 times 7p.   [p]

10   What is the remainder when 20 is divided by 3 ?   [ ]

C

Answer

1   Jane's date of birth is 3.11.'71. Write the name of the month in which she was born.   _____

2   Write the correct sign >, < or = in place of ●.
5 × 6 ● 6 × 1 × 5   [ ]

3   Jack received 14p change after spending 36p. Which coin did he give the shopkeeper ?   [p]

4   By how many cm is $\frac{1}{2}$ m greater than $\frac{1}{4}$ m ?   [cm]

5   How many 5-litre cans can be filled from 45 litres of oil ?   [ ]

6   John spent 6p which was one tenth of his money. How much was all of his money ?   [p]

7   A bus departs at 4.45 p.m. and arrives at the first stop 20 minutes later. Write in figures its arrival time.   [p.m.]

8   The bus fare is 11p. What change is given from 1 TWENTY ?   [p]

9

7 kg	5 kg	11 kg
9$\frac{1}{2}$ kg		13 kg

Which of these weights is nearest to 10 kg ?   [kg]

10   The product of two numbers is 48. One of the numbers is 6. What is the other ?   [ ]

Turn back to page 16 and work for the second time Progress Test 1.

Enter the result and the date on the chart.

21

A

Answer

1   70 = tens

2   Write in figures three hundred.

3   200 + 500

4   700 − 400

5   13p + 18p   p

6   $\frac{1}{10}$ of a FIFTY   p

7   25p − 9p   p

8   (6 × 6) + 5

9   7 = 28 ÷

10 16 + 5 − 9

B

Answer

1   Write the missing number in this series.
    300, 400, 500, ▦, 700

2   Find the total of
    30p + 6p + 4p + 10p   p

3   What number is 11 more than 59?

4   How many cm in 3 m?   cm

5   How many hours from 10 a.m. to 2 p.m.?   h

6   What fraction of this whole one is shaded?

7   By how much is 22p less than 3 TENS?   p

8   6 + 6 + 6 + 6 + 6 + 6 + 6 =   × 6

    =

9   How many quarters in 2$\frac{1}{2}$?

10 Find the difference between 30 and the sum of 19 and 7.

C

Answer

1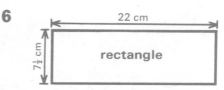

    Estimate which of the lines **X**, **Y** or **Z** measures 7 cm.

2   £1·00 = 100p. How many pennies are worth £5·00?   p

3   What is the date 4 days after 29 December?

4   Of 35 marbles, one fifth are blue and the rest red.
    How many are red?

5   How many 6p oranges can be bought for 2 TWENTIES, 1 TEN and 4 pennies?

6
    22 cm

    7$\frac{1}{2}$ cm   rectangle

    By how many cm is the length of the rectangle greater than the width?   cm

7   What number when divided by 3 gives 8 for the answer?

8   What fraction of these beads is white?
    ●○●●●●○●

9   How much is needed to give 7 girls 6p each?   p

10 $\frac{1}{2}$ kg of potatoes cost 14p.
    Find the cost of 1$\frac{1}{2}$ kg.   p

22

A

Answer

		TENS	p

1 83p = ▦ TENS ▦ pennies

2 Write in figures
four hundred and eighty.

3 250 + 100

4 720 − 100

5 One third of 27p   [ ] p

6 21 − 5 − 7

7 30 − 3 = 40 − ▦

8 10 × 2 = ▦ × 4

9 6 TWOS + 3p = ▦ FIVES

10 31 ÷ 4 = 7 rem. ▦

B

Answer

1 How many times greater than
10 is 100?

2 Write the missing number in
this series.
490, 590, 690, ▦, 890

3 One tenth of a line measures
$5\frac{1}{2}$ cm. Find the total length.   [ ] cm

4  Write this
as a morning
time.
Use a.m.
or p.m.

5 How many TENS in £1·00?

6 Find the difference between
$\frac{3}{4}$ and 2.

7 How many metres in 600 cm?   [ ] m

8 Divide 27 into three equal parts.
Find one part.

9 Find the total of 300, 150 and
500.

10 Multiply 8 by 5 and then
add 3.

C

Answer

1 A number minus 7 equals 19.
What is the number?

2 By how many pennies is
£1·38 more than £1·00?   [ ] p

3   The rectangle is
twice as long
as it is wide.
Find its width.   [ ] cm

4 Two coins together
make £1·00.
What are the coins?   [ ] p [ ] p

5 What number when divided
by 10 gives the answer
8 rem. 9?

6 John has these coins in his
money box.

How much has he altogether?   [ ] p

7 How many days are there from
28th May to 4th June?
(Do not count 28th May.)

8 A bucket, when a quarter full,
holds $3\frac{1}{2}$ litres.
How many litres will it hold
when three-quarters full?   [ ] ℓ

9 3 biscuits cost 12p.
How much is paid for 4 biscuits?   [ ] p

10 Which of these lengths is
nearest to 60 cm?
$\frac{1}{2}$ m, $62\frac{1}{2}$ cm, $58\frac{1}{2}$ cm, 66 cm   [ ] cm

A

                    Answer

1 $77 + 30$

2   Write in words the number 203.

_____

3 $450 + 300$

4 $890 - 500$

5 $6\overline{)48}$

6   £1·25 = £1 + ▨ pennies   **p**

7   23 − ▨ = 17

8   1 FIFTY + 1 TEN = ▨ TWENTIES

9 $7 \times$ ▨ $= 21$

10 $40 + 6 = 30 +$ ▨

B

                    Answer

1   Find the sum of £1·00 and 45p.   **£**

2   How many cm in 5 metres?   **cm**

3   Complete this series.
    310, 210, 110, ▨

4   Take 40 from 200.

5   Add the odd numbers between 16 and 20.

6   How many hours from 11.00 a.m. to midnight?   **h**

7   Find the change from £1 after spending 85p.   **p**

8   How many times less than 300 is 30?

9   What is the difference between a whole one and three tenths?

10 $9 + 7 = 20 - x$
Find the value of x.

C

                    Answer

1   £1 is worth a FIFTY and some FIVES. How many FIVES?

2   What number is 10 more than 490?

3   The lengths of four lines are $8\frac{1}{2}$ cm, $4\frac{1}{2}$ cm, 17 cm, 24 cm. Find the difference between the shortest and longest line.   **cm**

4   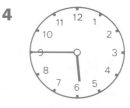 The time on this clock is 20 minutes slow. What is the correct time?

5   48p is divided exactly among 6 children. How much each?   **p**

6   There are 4 glasses of squash in a litre. How many litres are needed to give 36 children a glass each?   **ℓ**

7   By how much is $\frac{1}{3}$ of 30p greater than $\frac{1}{5}$ of 30p?   **p**

8   ● stands for a missing sign, $+, -, \times$ or $\div$.
    $8 \times 0 = 4$ ● 4
What is the correct sign?

9   Mother buys 2 oranges at 7p each. How much change out of a FIFTY does she receive?   **p**

10   H   T   U   Write in words the number shown on this abacus picture.

A

Answer

1 400 + 20 + 6

2 £0·72 = ▦ pennies ____ p

3 30 ÷ 6

4 5 × 3 × 0

5 1 m 38 cm = ▦ cm ____ cm

6 97 − 50

7 13 quarters = ▦

8 4p + ▦p = 1 TWENTY ____ p

9 100 − 20

10 20 ÷ 3 = 6 rem. ▦

B

Answer

1 How many tens are there in 380?

2 What number is 1 more than 499?

3 By how many cm is 1 m 55 cm longer than 1 metre? ____ cm

4 How many TWOS are worth 1 FIFTY?

5 Share 9 FIVES equally among 5 girls. How many pennies each? ____ p

6 £1·00 = ▦ TWENTIES

7 How many minutes from 11.40 a.m. until dinner time at half past 12? ____ min

8 1½ = ▦ tenths

9 What is the value of the 5 in the number 542?

10 Complete this series. 133, 123, 113, 103, ▦

C

Answer

1 A TV programme begins at 5.40 p.m. and lasts for 25 minutes. At what time does it finish?

2 Re-arrange the figures 6, 9, 8 to make the largest possible number.

3 What fraction of this shape is shaded?

4 Write as £s this sum of money. £3 and 27p ____ £

5 A piece of wood is 18 cm shorter than 1 m. How long is the piece of wood? ____ cm

6 On a bus Joan pays half fare which is 8p. How much is the total fare for mother and Joan? ____ p

7 Alan's date of birth is 3.9.78 Mary is 6 years older than Alan. In which year was she born?

8 Tim bought a mini-car for 68p. How much change did he receive from £1? ____ p

9 ⅓ of a sum of money is 12p. How much is ⅔ of the money? ____ p

10 cm
Each cm on this line stands for 8 m. What length in m does the line stand for? ____ m

Turn back to page 16 and work for the third time Progress Test 1. Enter the result and the date on the chart.

A

Answer

1. $29 + 7$ [ ]

2. $25 - 6$ [ ]

3. $600 + 70 + 6$ [ ]

4. $145\,cm = $ ▦ m ▦ cm [m | cm]

5. $9 \times 2 = $ ▦ $\times 6$ [ ]

6. $1\frac{1}{2} - \frac{3}{4}$ [ ]

7. How many days in June? [ ]

8. $£0.14 = $ ▦ pennies [p]

9. $41 \div 6 = 6$ rem. ▦ [ ]

10. $(7 \times 4) + 3$ [ ]

B

Answer

1. Add together 3p, 6p and 14p. [p]

2. $8 \times 6 = $ ▦ tens ▦ units [T | U]

3. By how many cm is $\frac{1}{2}$ m longer than 38 cm? [cm]

4. Find the missing numbers. $329 = $ ▦ tens ▦ units [T | U]

5. Increase £1·07 by 3p. [£]

6. What number is 20 less than 600? [ ]

7. Complete this series.
$\frac{1}{3}, \frac{2}{3}, 1, 1\frac{1}{3}, 1\frac{2}{3},$ ▦ [ ]

8. Share 28p equally among 4 boys. [p]

9. How many minutes from 8.55 a.m. to 9.20 a.m.? [min]

10. £1·00 is worth 4 TWENTIES and ▦p. [p]

C

Answer

1. What is the eighth letter in the alphabet? [ ]

2. Which coin has the same value as £0·05? [p]

3. What number when divided by 3 gives 9 for the answer? [ ]

4.  By how many kg is bag A heavier than bag B? [kg]

5. 132 children each give 1p to the school fund. Write the total as £s. [£]

6.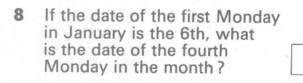
25 cm.

At what measurement is the middle point of a line of this length? [cm]

7. By how much is 95p less than £1·05? [p]

8. If the date of the first Monday in January is the 6th, what is the date of the fourth Monday in the month? [ ]

9. Which of these parts of a cake is the largest? $\frac{1}{4}, \frac{1}{2}$ or $\frac{1}{3}$ [ ]

10.

This is a row of stamps. How many are there in a sheet of 9 such rows? [ ]

A

Answer

1 24 − 8

2 3 + 39

3 (8 × 6) + 4

4 700 + 40 + 2

5 1 m 44 cm = ▦ cm   cm

6 10 × 4 = 8 × ▦

7 £1·00 + 6p   £

8 Three quarters of 1 hour
    = ▦ minutes   min

9 24 ÷ ▦ = 8

10 5 × 0 = 6 − ▦

B

Answer

1 How many tens in 400?

2 Divide 42 into 6 equal parts.
    Find one part.

3 Find the product of 9 and 4.

4 From £1·00 take 12p.   p

5 What number is 10 more
    than 192?

6 1 FIFTY + ▦ FIVES = £1·00

7 Complete the series.
    115, 110, 105, 100, ▦

8 By how many cm is ½ m
    longer than 26 cm?   cm

9 Write this time in figures.
    A quarter to eight in the
    evening.

10 What is the value of the figure
    underlined in the number 3_6_7?

C

Answer

1 In a class there were 26
    children. 8 of them were girls.
    How many were boys?

2 A truck travels 40 kilometres
    on 10 litres of petrol.
    How many km will it
    travel on 100 litres?   km

3 By how much is the largest of
    these sums of money greater
    than the smallest?
    £0·96, £1·10, £0·98, £1·07   p

4 Which of these numbers will
    divide exactly into 21 without
    a remainder?
    2, 3, 4, 5, 6

5 Name the month of the year
    which comes before August. _____

6 How many FIVES must be
    added to 80p to make
    £1·00?

7 20 people can travel on a minibus.
    How many such buses are
    needed to carry 100 people?

8 What is the cost of $1\frac{1}{2}$ m of
    tape at 18p per metre?   p

9 Mother has a FIFTY and 8
    pennies in her purse. She
    spends 39p.
    How much has she left?   p

10 The triangle has
3 equal sides. The
total length of
the sides is 12 cm.
What is the
length of one side?   cm

triangle

27

A

Answer

1   $300 + 20 + 7$

2   $(6 \times 3) + 2$

3   $24 \div \blacksquare = 4$

4   $1\ m\ 9\ cm = \blacksquare\ cm$ | cm |

5   $\frac{1}{3}$ of 21p | p |

6   $209 = \blacksquare$ tens 9 units | tens |

7   Write as £s;
two pounds 20 pence. | £ |

8   $106 - 20$

9   $\frac{1}{2}$ hour + 15 min = $\blacksquare$ min | min |

10 £1·00 − 16p | p |

B

Answer

1   Complete this series.
407, 307, 207, 107, $\blacksquare$

2   Find the total of 19, 7 and 5.

3   How many cm in $2\frac{1}{2}$ m? | cm |

4   How many
minutes to
the next
hour? | min |

5   By how much is 76p
greater than 50p? | p |

6   $202 = (20 \times \blacksquare) + 2$

7   Add four to nought times
five.

8   What must be added to 86p
to make £1·00? | p |

9   How many $\frac{1}{2}$ kg in 8 kg?

10 $68p = 5\ TENS + \blacksquare\ TWOS$

C

Answer

1   60 chairs are arranged in rows
of 10.
How many rows?

2   Paul spent 10p and 8p.
He had 5p left.
How much had he at first? | p |

3   A ——— 18 cm ——— C ——— B
27 cm

If the line AB is 27 cm long
and the line AC is 18 cm
long, how long is CB? | cm |

4   Which two of these sums of
money when added together
make 40p?
11p, 12p, 19p, 28p | p | p |

5   The difference between two
numbers is 9. The smaller
number is 18.
What is the larger number?

6   $\frac{3}{4}$ of my money is 27p.
What is $\frac{1}{4}$ of my money? | p |

7   A shop closes from 12.30 p.m.
until 2.00 p.m.
For how many hours
and minutes is the
shop closed? | h   min |

8   Find the cost of 2 kg of
potatoes at 20p per $\frac{1}{2}$ kg. | p |

9   What number when multiplied
by 5 will give a product of 100?

10 John pays 48p for a toy with an
equal number of FIVES and
pennies.
How many of each coin does
he use to pay for it?

Turn back to page 16 and work
for the fourth time Progress Test 1.
Enter the result and the date
on the chart.

28

A

Answer

1 Write in figures the number five hundred and seven.

2 194 + 8

3 ⅙ of 24p [ ] p

4 403 cm = ▦ m ▦ cm [m   cm]

5 700 − 90

6 £1·54 = ▦ pence [ ] p

7 (6 × 6) + 5

8 ▦ ÷ 4 = 7 rem. 3

9 1 FIFTY + 3 TENS + 2 TWOS [ ] p

10 10 × 10 × 10

B

Answer

1 What number must be added to 52 to make 70 ?

2 To £1·06 add 40p. [£]

3 From £1·58 take 16p. [£]

4 Increase 8½ cm five times. [cm]

5 Find the remainder when 41 is divided by 6.

6 How many quarters in 5½ ?

7 Complete this series.
   94, 96, 98, 100, ▦

8 Name the month which is 3 months after November. _____

9 How many hundreds in 1000 ?

10 Share 36p equally among 4 boys. How much each? [ ] p

C

Answer

1 Which two of these sums of money when added together make 50p?
   13p, 18p, 27p, 32p [ ] p [ ] p

2 How many times is the 5 in 51 greater than the 5 in 15 ?

3 A petrol tank which holds 60 litres is ¾ full.
   How many more litres will it take ? [ ] ℓ

4 [square] The total length of the four sides of the square is 38 cm.
   Find the length of one side. [ ] cm

5 A TV programme starts at 5.45 and ends 35 min later. At what time does it finish ?

6 Jean's date of birth is 3.3.'79. How old was she on the 3rd March 1985?

7 | £1·10   95p   £0·98   £1·05 |
   Which of these amounts of money is nearest to £1·00 ? [£]

8 Three numbers when added together total 639. One number is 9 and another is 600. Find the third.

9 What fraction of the shape is shaded ?

10 5 chocolate biscuits cost 25p. How much is paid for 2 biscuits ? [ ] p

Next work Progress Test 2 on page 30.
Enter the result and the date on the chart.

PROGRESS TEST 2

Write the numbers 1 to 20 down the side of a sheet of paper.
Write alongside these numbers the **answers only** to the following questions.
Work as quickly as you can.
Time allowed — **10 minutes.**

1   7 + ▓ = 15

2   23 minus 9

3   There are 4 apples in a bag. How many apples are there in 6 bags?

4   Share 1 TWENTY and 2 TWOS equally among 4 girls.
How much each?

5   There are 10 stamps in a row. How many stamps are there in
a sheet of 10 rows?

6   Write in figures the sum of
five hundreds, seven tens and three units.

7   What number is 5 more than 199?

8   Take 7 from 403.

9   Which of these numbers will divide by 5 without a remainder?
16, 23, 35, 39, 48

10   How many 10p coins are given in exchange for £3·60?

11 $\frac{1}{6}$ of the length of a piece of wood measures 9 cm.
What is its whole length?

12   The time shown on a clock is 8.05 but it is 20 minutes fast.
Find the correct time.

13   Find in £s the total value of the coins in the box.

14   How much change from £1 after buying oranges for 12p
and apples for 27p?

15   A parcel has a mass of 25 kg. Another parcel is $6\frac{1}{2}$ kg lighter.
Find the mass of this parcel.

16   A length of cloth measures 208 cm. Write this length in m and cm.

17   Find the total number of days in the last two months of the year.

18   John puts 9 conkers in each of 5 boxes. He has 4 conkers left.
How many has he altogether?

19   1 litre of oil costs 34p. Find the cost of 3 litres.

20

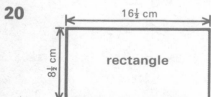

Find in cm the distance all round
the rectangle.

PROGRESS TEST 2 RESULTS CHART

You will work Progress Test 2 at **four** different times. When you first work the test
    (a) colour the first column to show the number of examples correct out of 20
    (b) enter the date.

Each time you work the test, enter the result and the date in the marked columns.

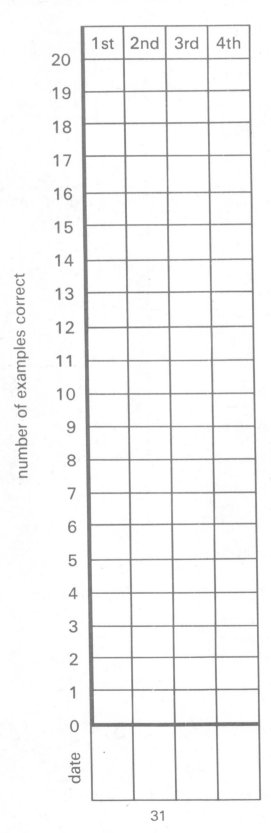

31

A

Answer

1 What is the number shown on the abacus picture?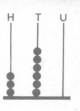

2 13 + 9

3 31 − 4

4 8 + 8 + 8 + 8 + 8 = ☐ ×8
   =

5 24 ÷ 4

6 £1·37 = £1 and ▦ p   p

7 307 cm = ▦ m ▦ cm   m   cm

8 1½ hours = ▦ minutes   min

9 29 ÷ 5 = 5 rem. ▦

10 4 FIVES and 9 TWOS   p

B

Answer

1 What is the missing number?
   582 = 500 + ▦ + 2

2 Increase 95p by 15p = £▦   £

3 What number is 7 less than 204?

4  Write in figures the time on the clock using a.m. or p.m.

   morning

5 How much change out of 20p after spending 8p?   p

6 How many FIVES are worth 3 TENS and 5 TWOS?

7 A piece of wood is cut into 3 equal parts. What fraction of the whole is each part?

8 Find the difference between the longest and shortest of these lengths.
   9½ cm, 26 cm, 18½ cm, 30½ cm   cm

9 How many whole ones in 20 quarters?

10 10 × ▦ p = £1·70   p

C

Answer

1 What number is added to 409 to make 449?   ☐

2 Alan has 6p and Jane has 14p more.
   How much have they altogether?   p

3 Monday is the 30th April. What is the date on the next Thursday?   _____

4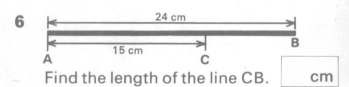
   19 kg   20½ kg   14 kg   22 kg

   Which of these weights is nearest to 20 kg?   kg

5 How much has Mother spent if she has 11p change out of a FIFTY?   p

6
   24 cm
   A   15 cm   C   B
   Find the length of the line CB.   cm

7 Jane has saved 8 TENS. How much more must she save to buy a book costing £1·25?   p

8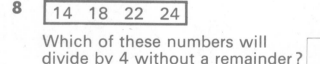
   14 18 22 24

   Which of these numbers will divide by 4 without a remainder?   ☐

9 6 tarts cost 42p. Find the cost of 1 tart.   p

10 The picture shows a layer of biscuits in a box. How many biscuits are in a box of 4 layers?   ☐

A

Answer

1 Write the number shown on this abacus picture.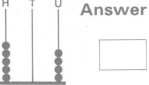

2 75 + 8

3 63 − 7

4 9 × 4 = 4 × ▓ = ▓

5 3 weeks = ▓ days

6 2 m 40 cm = ▓ cm   **cm**

7 (6 × 0) + 5

8 23 ÷ 3 = ▓ rem. ▓   **rem.**

9 Three pounds 29p = £▓   **£**

10 One thousand = 100 × ▓

B

Answer

1 What number is 300 less than 780?

2 Decrease £1·15 by 20p.   **p**

3 Find the total of 8p, 9p, 10p. **p**

4 How many fives are there in 500?

5 What is the time ¼ hour after 10.50?

6 How many is ¾ of 16?

7 Find the missing sum of money. ▓p ÷ 5 = 7p   **p**

8 How many FIVES have the same value as 2 TWENTIES and 5 TWOS?

9 Divide a length of 36 cm into 6 equal parts. What is the length of each part?   **cm**

10 Take 37 cm from ½ metre. How many cm are left?   **cm**

C

Answer

1 The distance between towns is measured in kilometres. 1 km = 1000 m. How many m are there in ½ km?   **m**

2 What number is taken from 376 to leave 306?

3 | $\frac{1}{3}$ | $\frac{1}{2}$ | $\frac{1}{4}$ | $\frac{1}{10}$ |

Which of these fractions is
(a) the largest   **(a)**

(b) the smallest?   **(b)**

4 The time on Jack's watch is 3.05 but the correct time is 2.50. Is his watch fast or slow and by how many minutes?   **min**

5 In a collection there were 309 pennies. Write this amount as £s.   **£**

6 | 28 | 20 | 16 | 12 |

Which of these numbers will divide by 3 without a remainder?

7 What number when multiplied by itself gives 25 as the answer?

8 One third of Tom's money is 9p.
Find (a) ⅔ of his money   **(a) p**

(b) all of his money.   **(b) p**

9 Sue received 15p change after spending 35p. Which coin did she give to the shopkeeper?   **p**

10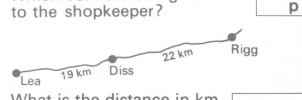

What is the distance in km from Lea to Rigg?   **km**

A

Answer

1 Write this number in figures.
seven hundred and eleven ☐

2 29 + 40 ☐

3 81 − 30 ☐

4 513 = ▦ tens 3 units ☐ tens

5 3 × 3 × 3 ☐

6 $\frac{1}{10}$ of 90p ☐ p

7 £1·00 = 1 FIFTY + ▦ TWOS ☐

8 1 km 300 m = ▦ m ☐ m

9 How many days in October? ☐

10 23 ÷ 5 = ▦ rem. ▦ ☐ rem.

B

Answer

1 What number is 8 more than 493? ☐

2 From 20 take the product of 4 and 5. ☐

3 Write the correct sign +, −, × or ÷ in place of ●.
13 − 7 = 12 ● 2 ☐

4  Write in figures the time on the clock using a.m. or p.m. ☐ p.m.

afternoon

5 By how much is 7p less than 19p? ☐ p

6 Find the total of £1·20 and £1·80. ☐ £

7 3 − $\frac{1}{4}$ − $\frac{1}{2}$ ☐

8 Write the missing number in this series.
350, 300, 250, 200, ▦, 100 ☐

9 By how many m is 400 m short of 1 km? ☐ m

10 Share 37p equally among 5 boys. How many pennies remain? ☐ p

C

Answer

1 What is the value of the 4 in the number 648? ☐

2 Apples cost 70p per kg. How much would be paid for 1$\frac{1}{2}$ kg? ☐ £

3 What number is two hundred more than 707? ☐

4  How many wafers are bought for 80p? ☐

5 Which of these numbers will divide by 10 without a remainder?
73, 85, 36, 90, 59 ☐

6 Mary's birthday is on 10th February, and David's is on 10th November.
How many months is Mary's birthday before David's? ☐

7 A man walked 6 km in 1 hour. How long would it take him to walk 18 km at the same speed? ☐ h

8 Sue saves 1 TWENTY each month. How much does she save in 1 year? ☐ £

9 $\frac{1}{2}$ of a sum of money is £1·40. Find $\frac{1}{4}$ of the money. ☐ p

10

10 of these circular discs are placed side by side as shown in the picture.
What is the total length? ☐ cm

A
Answer

1. Write this number in words.
   500 + 9 _____

2. 50 + 48

3. 70 − 29

4. 239 = ▦ hundreds ▦ units | H | U |

5. (8 × 1) + 5

6. ⅕ of 35p   p

7. £1·00   9 TENS and ▦ TWOS

8. 1250 m   1 km ▦ m   m

9. 1 h 20 min + ▦ min = 2 h   min

10. 37 ÷ 10 = ▦ rem. ▦   rem.

B
Answer

1. What number is 10 less than 1000?

2. Find the difference between 1¾ and 3.

3. What number is equal to (9 × 6) + 3?

4. Find the change from 3 TENS after spending 18p and 6p.   p

5. From £1·30 take 50p.   p

6. By how many m is 1405 m greater than 1 km?   m

7. What is the missing number?
   ▦ ÷ 4 = 4 rem. 3

8. Find the total value of these coins.

   p

9. 2 × 2 × 2 × 2

10. 1000 grams (g) = 1 kilogram (kg).

    How many g in ½ kg?   g

C
Answer

1. In a bag there are 9 pennies and the same number of TWOS.
   How much are all the coins worth?   p

2. Some oranges were cut into quarters. There were then 40 pieces.
   How many oranges were cut?

3. 505 people were at a concert. 200 were men, 200 were women and the rest children.
   How many children were there?

4. 4 kg cost 48p.
   Find the price per kg.   p

5.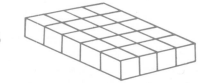

   The picture shows a layer of wooden bricks. How many bricks are there in 2 layers?

6. Tim measures 142 cm in height. By how many cm is he taller than 1 m?   cm

7. John leaves school on the bus at 3.40 p.m. He arrives home at a quarter past four.
   How many minutes does the journey take?   min

8. Which of these numbers will divide by 5 without a remainder?
   23, 40, 17, 34, 53

9. A van travels 30 km in 1 hour. How far will it travel in 4 hours at this speed?   km

10. Which of these shapes A, B, C or D is a rectangle?

Turn back to page 30 and work for the second time Progress Test 2. Enter the result and the date on the chart.

A

		Answer
1	$200 + 300 + 72$	
2	One thousand = $(4 \times 100) +$ ▨	
3	$4 \times 10 = 5 \times$ ▨	
4	$17 - 9 = 12 -$ ▨	
5	£0·37 = ▨ p	p
6	How many g in $1\frac{1}{2}$ kg?	g
7	$26 + 13 + 7$	
8	$24 \div 6 = 16 \div$ ▨	
9	Twice $6\frac{1}{4}$ litres	ℓ
10	$\frac{1}{10}$ kg = ▨ g	g

B

Answer

1 What number is added to 306 to make 366?

2 Double 9 and then add 7.

3 By how much is 82p less than £1·00? ____ p

4 What fraction of 1 kg is 200 g?

5 How many minutes from the time on the clock to half past 5? ____ min

6 Find the total length of 27 cm, 40 cm and 8 cm. ____ cm

7 Write the name of the sixth month in the year. _____

8 By how many pennies are 5 FIVES less than 4 TENS? ____ p

9 How many times can a length of 6 cm be cut from 54 cm?

10 | 45   56   43   58 |

Which of these numbers is nearest to 50?

C

Answer

1 Saxby 17km   Danby 9km   How far is it from Saxby to Danby? ____ km

2 Which two of these sums of money when added together make 20p?
6p, 9p, 8p, 14p ____ p ____ p

3 1 kg of fish costs £1·80. Find the cost of 100 g. ____ p

4 Which of these numbers will divide into 27 without a remainder?
6, 5, 4, 3

5 Jill saves a TEN each day for a fortnight. Find her total savings. £ ____

6 Guess (estimate) which of these lines X, Y or Z measures 5 cm.
X ——————————————
Y ——————————————
Z ——————

7 John loses 4 of these marbles. What fraction of all the marbles has he lost?

8 How many hours and minutes after midday is the time on the clock? ____ h ____ min

9 A car travels at 50 kilometres per hour. At this speed how long will it take to travel 250 km? ____ h

10 Joan has these coins in her money box.

How much more must she save to have £1·00? ____ p

A

Answer

1 H T U

Write in words the number shown on the abacus picture.

2 40 + 30 + 7

3 (8 × 4) − 12

4 $\frac{1}{10}$ of five hundred

5 19 − 6 = 7 + ▧

6 $\frac{1}{3}$ of 6 TENS = ▧ p ___ p

7 90 − 40 − 3

8 204 = ▧ tens ▧ units

T	U

9 7 × 6 × 0

10 1 kg − 200 g ___ g

B

Answer

1 Rearrange the figures 7, 3, 5 to make the smallest possible number.

2 Find the number which is thirty more than four times nought.

3 Share £1·50 equally among 10 children. How much each? ___ p

4 Find the difference between 700 g and 1 kg. ___ g

5 What fraction of the strip is shaded?

6 How many minutes are there from a quarter past twelve to one o'clock? ___ min

7 5p plus 3 TWOS plus 4 FIVES ___ p

8 Find the change from 30p after spending 12p and 9p. ___ p

9 10 × 4 × 10

10 1 litre (ℓ) = 1000 millilitres (mℓ). How many mℓ in $\frac{1}{2}$ litre? ___ mℓ

C

Answer

1 A daily newspaper costs 20p. How much is paid for the days Monday to Saturday? £ ___

2 How many $\frac{1}{2}$ litre bottles can be filled from 8 litres of milk?

3 bus ticket
Number
390
50p

What is the number on the bus ticket when 20 more have been sold?

4 How much would be paid for the 20 tickets? £ ___

5 There are 30 beads in a bag. $\frac{2}{3}$ of them are red. How many is that?

6 On this line 1 cm stands for 5 km.

cm

How many km does the whole line stand for? ___ km

7 6 children shared a prize equally. They each received 8p and there were 2 pennies left. What was the value of the prize? ___ p

8 Jane is 1 m 35 cm tall and Jill is 142 cm tall. By how many cm is Jill taller than Jane? ___ cm

9 A notebook and pencil cost 70p. The pencil cost 11p. How much did the notebook cost? ___ p

10 square

A square has

▧ equal sides,

▧ right angles.

A

Answer

1 Write in words the number which equals 40 tens. _____

2 19 + 17 + 1

3 65 − 35

4 16p × 2 ___ p

5 3)‾28‾ ▦ rem. ▦ ___ rem.

6 1 km − 40 m ___ m

7 40p + £2·00 ___ £

8 3 × 1¼

9 100 + 60 + 50

10 ⅕ of 1 kg = ▦ g ___ g

B

Answer

1 Find the sum of 480 and 30.

2 9 + 8 = x + 10 What is the value of x?

3 How many months are there from 30th April to 30th November?

4 From 2 m take 45 cm. ___ m ___ cm

5 How many TWOS are changed for 5 TENS?

6 What is the time 3 hours later than the time on the clock?

7 By how many g is 380 g less than ½ kg? ___ g

8 48½ cm   53 cm   46 cm   51 cm

Which of these lengths is nearest to ½ m? ___ cm

9 Find the total of 25p and £1·80. ___ £

10 One third of 24 litres ___ ℓ

C

Answer

1 180 envelopes are put into packets of 10. How many packets?

2 35   15   46   25   90

Which of these numbers will divide by both 5 and 10 without a remainder?

3 28th March is the first day of a holiday which ends on 5th April. How many days?

4 An orange costs 6p. How many oranges can be bought for 3 TENS and 3 TWOS?

5 [9 biscuits] [18 biscuits] All the biscuits are shared equally among 3 children. How many biscuits each?

6 Peter cycled 100 kilometres in 5 hours. What was his speed in kilometres per hour (km/h)? ___ km/h

7 BUTTER 250g How many such packets can be made from 1 kg of butter?

8 By how many is 1/10 of 70 less than ¼ of 80?

9 Mother gave £1 to pay for her groceries. She received in change 1 TWO, 6 pennies and 1 FIVE. Find the cost of the groceries. ___ p

10 Which of these angles A, B, C or D is a right angle?

A

Answer

1. $20 + 80 + 30 + 4$

2. Write in words the number which equals 15 tens and 3.

3. $100 - 76$

4. $(6 \times 6) + 5$

5. $20p - 11p$ p

6. $50 \div 6 = $ ▦ rem. ▦   rem.

7. $\frac{1}{2}$ of $3\frac{1}{2}$ kg   kg

8. $68p = 3$ TWENTIES $+$ ▦ TWOS

9. $5 + 9 + 7 = 9 + $ ▦ $+ 5$

10. $£1·46 - 90p$ p

B

Answer

1. What number is equal to the sum of ten tens and eighteen?

2. Multiply by 6 the difference between 13 and 8.

3. What is the next even number which is greater than 48?

4. Find the cost of $1\frac{1}{2}$ kg of fish at 90p per $\frac{1}{2}$ kg.   £

5. What fraction of this shape is shaded?

6. By how many m is 1 km 400 m less than 2 km?   m

7. Find the change from a FIFTY after spending 14p.   p

8. Which of these measurements is nearest to 1 m?
   85 cm, 93 cm, 102 cm, 96 cm

9. What number when divided by 4 gives the answer 7 rem. 3?

10. How many times can 3 be taken from 21?

C

Answer

1. Find the total cost of 2 oranges at 7p each and 2 at 9p each.   p

2. What is the smallest number which can be divided by both 3 and 4 without a remainder?

3. A square has 4 equal sides each measuring 1 cm.
   How many such squares could be fitted into a rectangle of these measurements?

   1cm ⟵————————— 16 cm —————————⟶

4. Peter spent 15p which was $\frac{3}{4}$ of his money.
   How much had he at first?   p

5. An 8 day holiday cruise started on 25th May.
   On what date did it end?

6. How much change out of a FIFTY after paying for $1\frac{1}{2}$ kg potatoes at 24p per kg?   p

7. Toffees are bought at 3 for 8p.
   How many for 2 TWENTIES?

8. A car travels 80 km on 10 litres of petrol.
   How many litres will be used for a journey of 240 km?   ℓ

9. Jane has 4p, Mary 11p and Sue 9p. If all their money is shared equally, how much will each have?   p

10. Tigby   28 km   Radley   Crosby

    The distance from Crosby via Tigby to Radley is 42 km.
    How far is it from Crosby to Tigby?   km

Turn back to page 30 and work for the third time Progress Test 2.

Enter the result and the date on the chart.

A

Answer

1   $(5 \times 100) + (3 \times 10)$

2   $6 + 20 + 7$

3   $(6 \times 5) + 3$

4   20 cm $- 5\frac{1}{2}$ cm   **cm**

5   $240 = 10 + $ ▒ $ + 200$

6   $\frac{1}{2}$ kg $- 100$ g   **g**

7   ▒ $\div 5 = 9$

8   $(16$ cm $- 8$ cm$) + 5$ cm   **cm**

9   1070 g $= 1$ kg ▒ g   **g**

10   $\frac{1}{3}$ of $12 + \frac{1}{4}$ of 20

B

Answer

1   What is the next odd number greater than 69 ?

2   From 403 take 10.

3   Divide 35 cm into 10 equal parts. What is the exact length of each part ?   **cm**

4   What number is added to 8 to make 278 ?

5   How many g in 1 kg 40 g ?   **g**

6   Write the missing sign $+, -, \times$ or $\div$ in place of the ●. $13 - 5 = 8$ ● 1

7   How many cm when 37 cm is added to $\frac{1}{2}$ metre ?   **cm**

8   $50p + 34p + 20p = $ £▒   **£**

9   In 42 there are 7 groups of 6. How many groups of 7 are there in 42 ?

10   What is the change from 2 TWENTIES after spending 29p ?   **p**

C

Answer

1   Seven hundred and sixteen cards were put into packets of 100. How many were left ?

2   A boy works $1\frac{1}{2}$ hours each day from Monday to Friday. How many hours does he work ?   **h**

3   Estimate which two of these lines W, X, Y or Z are of equal length.

   W ▬▬▬▬▬▬▬▬
      X ▬▬▬▬▬▬▬▬▬▬▬
   Y ▬▬▬▬▬▬▬▬▬▬▬
      Z ▬▬▬▬▬▬▬▬▬▬

4   100 g of cheese cost 20p. Find the cost of $\frac{1}{2}$ kg.   **£**

5   The distance between two towns is 83 km. Write this distance to the nearest 10 km.   **km**

6   What is the total cost of 4 tins of polish at 40p per tin ?   **£**

7 | rectangle |

A rectangle has
▒ pairs of equal opposite sides,
▒ right angles.

8   By how much per metre is 48p per metre cheaper than 57p per metre ?   **p**

9   A bag of apples has a mass of 1 kg 200 g. Write the mass in grams.   **g**

10   Find the total value of these coins.

  p

A
Answer

1   400 − 200 − 50

2   (7 × 10) + 6

3   One fifth of thirty

4   45 ÷ 6 = ▦ rem. ▦ | rem. |

5   2 × $\frac{3}{4}$

6   750 g = 500 g + ▦ g | g |

7   30p + 60p = £1·00 − ▦ p | p |

8   45p = ▦ FIVES

9   $\frac{1}{2}$ m + 18 cm | cm |

10 70 + 9 = ▦ + 60

B
Answer

1   What number when multiplied by 6 gives sixty as the answer?

2   How much is added to 3 TWOS and 1 FIVE to make 20p? | p |

3   To the product of 3 and 6 add 5.

4   What is the difference between the largest and smallest of these numbers? $1\frac{1}{2}$, $\frac{3}{4}$, 4, $3\frac{1}{4}$

5   From £1·15 take 90p. | p |

6   What length is 5 cm less than $\frac{1}{2}$ m? | cm |

7   When 32p is divided equally among 5 boys how many pennies are left?

8   How many minutes from the time on the clock to 10.50? | min |

9   Re-arrange the numbers 4, 6, 9 to make the largest possible odd number.

10 $\frac{1}{2}$ kg is ▦ g less than 625 g. | g |

C
Answer

1   How many 50p coins are exchanged for £3·00?

2    John's span measures 12 cm. Find the length of 5 spans. | cm |

3   A jug holds $\frac{1}{2}$ litre. How many times can it be filled from a jar holding 8 litres?

4   In a school there are 523 pupils. Write this number to the nearest 100.

5   A train travels at 80 km/h. How many km will it travel in 15 min at this speed? | km |

6 | potatoes |
    | 19p per kg |
    | 23p per kg |
    Mother orders 8 kg of potatoes. How much will she save if she has the cheaper kind? | p |

7   Tom leaves home at 8.30 a.m. and returns at 4.30 p.m. For how many hours is he away from home? | h |

8   Mother spends 68p. She has left in her purse 4 TENS and 2 FIVES. How much had she at first? | £ |

9 | 15   21   30   39 |

    Which of these numbers will divide by both 3 and 6 without a remainder?

10 The distance round the triangle is 25 cm. Two sides each measure 9 cm. What is the length of the third side? | cm |

9 cm   9 cm   triangle

A

Answer

1. 50 tens + 8 units

2. 3 + 3 + 3 + 3 + 3 + 3 + 3 + 3

3. $\frac{1}{4}$ of 1 km = ▨ metres   **m**

4. £1·00 − 45p   **p**

5. 10 × 0 = 8 × ▨

6. 489 + 20

7. $\frac{1}{2}$ kg = 850 g − ▨ g   **g**

8. 1 = $\frac{1}{5}$ + ▨

9. How many days in August and September together?

10. 85 cm + ▨ cm = 1 metre   **cm**

B

Answer

1. 5 more than 17 minus 8.

2. Add the even numbers between 9 and 15.

3. How many TENS are worth £2·70?

4. 8 × 5 = 5 × ▨

5. 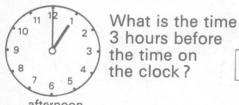 What is the time 3 hours before the time on the clock?

afternoon

6. When 36 is divided by a number the answer is 9. What is the number?

7. Find the cost of 5 tins of fruit at 30p per tin.   **£**

8. One tenth of 460.

9. From 2 m take 75 cm.   **m**   **cm**

10. Find the difference between 5 FIVES and 7 TWOS.   **p**

C

Answer

1. How many envelopes are there in 12 packets each containing 20 envelopes?

2. Jane has 18p which is $\frac{3}{4}$ of her money. How much is half of her money?   **p**

3. A length of cloth measures 1 m 24 cm. It is cut into 2 equal pieces. Find the length of each piece.   **cm**

4. 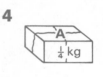 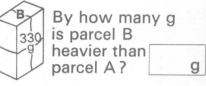 By how many g is parcel B heavier than parcel A?   **g**

5. Philip's birthday is in October. Jane is 5 months older than Philip. In which month is her birthday?

6. How much more than £1·00 did Mother spend after paying for 1$\frac{1}{2}$ kg apples at 40p per $\frac{1}{2}$ kg?   **p**

7. The petrol tank in a car when full, holds 60 litres. It is $\frac{1}{4}$ full. How many more litres are required to fill it?   **ℓ**

8. 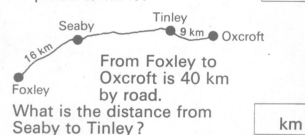 From Foxley to Oxcroft is 40 km by road. What is the distance from Seaby to Tinley?   **km**

9. Mary changes 18 pennies and 6 TWOS for FIVES. How many FIVES did she receive?

10. Which of these angles A, B, C or D is less than a right angle?

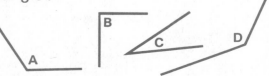

A

Answer

1 614 = ▨ tens 4 units | tens |

2 Half of (15 − 7) | |

3 130 cm + 70 cm = ▨ metres | m |

4 $4\frac{3}{4}$ = ▨ quarters | |

5 (8p × 6) + 2p | p |

6 $1 - \frac{7}{10}$ = ▨ | |

7 24 ÷ 4 = 3 × ▨ | |

8 £1·00 − 16p | p |

9 630 − 50 | |

10 1 kg = ▨ g + 750 g | g |

B

Answer

1 What is the value of the figure underlined in the number 8**6**3? | |

2 To 23p add 17p and 5p. | p |

3 Write the missing sign +, −, × or ÷ in place of the ●. 6 tens ● 8 units = 52 | |

4 Decrease £1·35 by 29p. | £ |

5 What is the missing number in this series? 48, 42, 36, 30, ▨ | |

6 By how many metres is 660 m more than $\frac{1}{2}$ km? | m |

7 How many times can 5 be subtracted from 40? | |

8 Divide £0·48 by 6. Write the answer as pennies. | p |

9 How many minutes in $2\frac{1}{2}$ hours? | min |

10 $\overset{2\ 0\ \text{rem.}\ 2}{3)\,▨}$ What is the missing number? | |

C

Answer

1 A piece of wire measures 40 cm. Find the length in m of 10 pieces. | m |

2 A girl practises playing her recorder for $\frac{3}{4}$ hour. She begins at 5.55 p.m. At what time does she finish? | |

3 | new laid eggs |
    | **6 for 50p** |
    How many eggs are bought for £2·00? | |

4 A side of a square measures $9\frac{1}{2}$ cm. Find the total length of its sides. | cm |

5 1 litre of water has a mass of 1 kilogram. What is the mass in grams of $\frac{1}{2}$ litre of water? | g |

6 £2·38 has the same value as £2. 3 TENS and some TWOS. How many TWOS? | |

7 John measures his pace which is 50 cm long. How many paces measure 7 m? | |

8 A sum of money is divided into two parts. One part is worth 7p and the other is worth three times as much. What is the sum of money? | p |

9 The mass of each of three parcels is 420 g, $\frac{1}{4}$ kg and 390 g. By how many g is the heaviest parcel greater than the lightest? | g |

10 Which of the angles A, B, C, D in this shape are greater than a right angle? | | | |

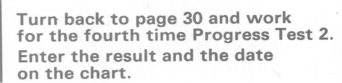

Turn back to page 30 and work for the fourth time Progress Test 2. Enter the result and the date on the chart.

A Write in words the number shown on each abacus picture.

 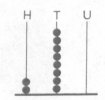 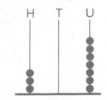 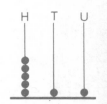

_____   _____   _____   _____

B Write in figures

five hundred

one hundred and sixty-three

four hundred and thirteen

nine hundred and forty

three hundred and five

two hundred and eighty-nine

eight hundred and twenty-four

one hundred and two

seven hundred and seventy

one thousand.

C

$400 + 60 + 3$

$700 + 80$

$600 + 1$

$300 + 10 + 9$

$500 + 20$

$100 + 16$

$379 = $ ▓ tens 9 units   tens

$404 = $ ▓ tens 4 units   tens

$230 = 2$ hundreds ▓ units   units

$865 = 8$ hundreds ▓ units   units

ADDITION

D
$7 + 2$
$5 + 5$
$3 + 6$
$0 + 9$
$2 + 8$
$8 + 3$
$5 + 9$
$7 + 4$
$2 + 9$
$4 + 8$
$6 + 5$
$8 + 8$
$7 + 6$
$9 + 9$
$6 + 8$
$6 + 6$
$8 + 5$
$3 + 9$
$8 + 9$
$9 + 6$

E
$16 + 3$
$2 + 18$
$5 + 14$
$11 + 8$
$7 + 13$
$15 + 7$
$13 + 8$
$5 + 16$
$18 + 4$
$6 + 19$
$17 + 7$
$6 + 14$
$19 + 4$
$5 + 18$
$7 + 19$
$15 + 5$
$29 + 8$
$7 + 26$
$8 + 27$
$4 + 29$

SUBTRACTION

F
$9 - 5$
$7 - 3$
$8 - 0$
$10 - 4$
$10 - 7$
$12 - 3$
$14 - 5$
$11 - 7$
$13 - 9$
$17 - 9$
$16 - 8$
$13 - 5$
$14 - 9$
$13 - 6$
$14 - 8$
$17 - 8$
$18 - 9$
$15 - 8$
$16 - 7$
$13 - 8$

G
$17 - 4$
$19 - 6$
$18 - 5$
$14 - 10$
$16 - 6$
$21 - 2$
$22 - 5$
$24 - 7$
$25 - 6$
$26 - 9$
$24 - 6$
$25 - 9$
$22 - 7$
$21 - 6$
$25 - 7$
$21 - 8$
$32 - 9$
$31 - 4$
$34 - 5$
$33 - 7$

'CHECKING-UP' TEST

A Write the missing number in each of these series.

270, 370, 470, 570, ▨

403, 303, 203, 103, ▨

360, 370, 380, 390, ▨

135, 125, 115, 105, ▨

How many times larger is

100 than 10 ?

1000 than 100 ?

300 than 3 ?

460 than 46 ?

Write the value of the figures underlined.

7̲06

85̲0

6̲03

ADDITION

B 20 + 50

10 + 90

39 + 40

70 + 18

95 + 6

75 + 30

92 + 9

150 + 50

247 + 100

180 + 20

396 + 10

199 + 1

298 + 5

106 + 7

509 + 4

SUBTRACTION

C 60 − 40

80 − 50

47 − 10

99 − 30

87 − 17

32 − 12

74 − 4

112 − 10

208 − 100

460 − 60

103 − 6

300 − 7

201 − 10

500 − 40

310 − 5

MULTIPLICATION   TABLES 2, 3, 4, 5, 6, 10   DIVISION

D 2 × 6

7 × 3

5 × 4

8 × 5

4 × 6

3 × 10

0 × 3

1 × 6

2 × 5

10 × 6

7 × 5

4 × 8

6 × 9

9 × 2

4 × 9

E (1 × 5) + 3

(3 × 4) + 2

(5 × 5) + 2

(7 × 10) + 6

(9 × 3) + 2

(8 × 6) + 5

(7 × 4) + 2

(6 × 6) + 4

(0 × 10) + 5

(1 × 8) + 4

(2 × 4) + 3

(6 × 3) + 2

(8 × 2) + 1

(5 × 6) + 4

(7 × 6) + 5

F 12 ÷ 2

15 ÷ 5

50 ÷ 10

18 ÷ 3

30 ÷ 6

24 ÷ 4

0 ÷ 3

35 ÷ 5

42 ÷ 6

16 ÷ 2

32 ÷ 4

70 ÷ 10

0 ÷ 5

21 ÷ 3

48 ÷ 6

G 15 ÷ 2   rem.

30 ÷ 4   rem.

37 ÷ 10   rem.

21 ÷ 5   rem.

25 ÷ 3   rem.

20 ÷ 6   rem.

3 ÷ 5   rem.

8 ÷ 6   rem.

64 ÷ 10   rem.

39 ÷ 4   rem.

19 ÷ 2   rem.

47 ÷ 5   rem.

40 ÷ 6   rem.

7 ÷ 10   rem.

29 ÷ 3   rem.

H

Find the total of 9, 7, 4 and 2.

29 minus 10

8 times 3

Increase 15 by 9.

Divide 36 into 4 equal parts.

What is the difference between 8 and 23 ?

Find the product of 9 and 10.

What number is added to 16 to make 25 ?

By how many is 18 less than 26 ?

What number when multiplied by 6 gives 42 as the answer ?

45

A

10p = ☐ FIVES ☐
       ☐ TWOS ☐

20p = ☐ TENS ☐
       ☐ FIVES ☐
       ☐ TWOS ☐

50p = ☐ TENS ☐
       ☐ FIVES ☐
       ☐ TWOS ☐

£1 = ☐ FIFTIES ☐
       ☐ TWENTIES ☐
       ☐ TENS ☐
       ☐ FIVES ☐
       ☐ TWOS ☐
       ☐ pennies ☐

B   By counting find the total value of the coins in each box.

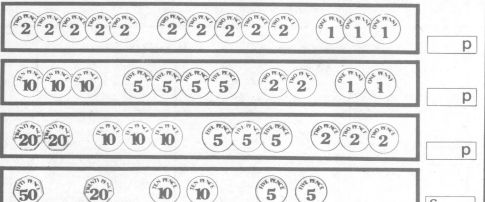

Row 1: 2 2 2 2 2   2 2 2 2 2   1 1 1   ☐ p

Row 2: 10 10 10   5 5 5 5   2 2   1 1   ☐ p

Row 3: 20 20   10 10 10   5 5 5   2 2 2   ☐ p

Row 4: 50   20   10 10   5 5   £ ☐

C

7 TENS	=	☐ p
8 FIVES	=	☐ p
12 TWOS	=	☐ p
2 TENS and 3 TWOS	=	☐ p
4 TWOS and 5p	=	☐ p
4 TENS and 6 FIVES	=	☐ p
1 FIFTY and 2 TWENTIES	=	☐ p

D

Find the change from a TEN after spending	Find the change from a TWENTY after spending	Find the change from a FIFTY after spending	Find the change from £1 after spending
4p ☐ p	16p ☐ p	44p ☐ p	93p ☐ p
8p ☐ p	12p ☐ p	38p ☐ p	85p ☐ p
6p ☐ p	14p ☐ p	22p ☐ p	78p ☐ p
2p ☐ p	18p ☐ p	19p ☐ p	61p ☐ p
5p ☐ p	15p ☐ p	36p ☐ p	54p ☐ p
3p ☐ p	11p ☐ p	25p ☐ p	42p ☐ p
1p ☐ p	7p ☐ p	14p ☐ p	36p ☐ p
7p ☐ p	3p ☐ p	9p ☐ p	19p ☐ p

E   Write the missing number of coins.

6 TWOS and 3 pennies = ☐ FIVES ☐
2 TENS and 5 TWOS = ☐ FIVES ☐
1 FIFTY and 3 TENS = ☐ TWENTIES ☐
1 FIFTY and 2 TWENTIES = ☐ TENS ☐

F   £1 is worth

4 TWENTIES and ☐ TENS ☐
1 FIFTY and ☐ TENS ☐
1 FIFTY, 1 TWENTY ☐ TENS ☐
1 FIFTY, 2 TWENTIES ☐ FIVES ☐